D1582108

£3.75

Dear boys and girls,
Hello again, from all your friends in Greendale village. This annual is packed with stories, games to play and things to make. Discover what a mess I made, when I tried a spot of DIY and find out what happened when Julian had an invitation to France. You can make peppermint creams and even learn some French.

Don't forget to try your hand at our special quiz. Remember, all the answers can be found in this annual.

All our love

Pat and Jess!

Dressing up

"Let me help."

1 Greendale was holding a Fun Day. Everyone was dressing in medieval costumes. The Reverend Timms was in charge and Pat was helping.

2 Ted Glen and Alf Thompson were dressed up as knights. But Ted was having some trouble with his helmet. "I'll put it on you," offered Pat.

3 Clever Peter Fogg had turned his tractor into a horse. "I have never heard of a horse that chugs like this one does," he laughed.

4 They were planning to hold a procession through the village. Pat was leading it and pulling the school float behind him.

5 All the children were excited. They were dressing up as Robin Hood and his band of merry men. Julian had been chosen to play Robin.

6 Katy Pottage was thrilled to be Maid Marion. Pat helped her climb on to the float. Tom was Will Scarlet. Even Jess had a part to play!

7 Colonel Forbes was the Sheriff of Nottingham. He tried to pull a fierce face at the children. But they just burst out laughing at him.

You look nice!

8 Miss Hubbard was playing the lady of the manor. She was riding beside the Sheriff in a carriage. "You look nice," said Pat, bowing.

9 It was soon time for the procession to start. But one of the floats was not ready. "Now everything is delayed," sighed Reverend Timms.

10 He tried to radio the others on the green to let them know, but his radio would not work. "I'll take a message by bike," Pat offered.

11 So Reverend Timms wrote a note and Pat cycled to the village. He did look ridiculous in his old costume, riding a pushbike.

12 "Thank you for telling us the procession will be late," said PC Selby. "Even in medieval costume, you are still delivering things!"

Kings and Queens

Can you guess who these characters are? They are all royals from these well-known nursery rhymes.

Sing a Song of Sixpence
The Queen of Hearts
Old King Cole

Fancy dress!

Tom and Katy are dressing up.

Tom is pretending to be a robot.
You will need two cardboard boxes. The larger box needs to be big enough to cover your body.
Cut a hole in the top and two more in the sides for your head and arms.
The second box should fit over your head. Make sure it is not too small. Cut a hole in the front to leave your face free. Ask a grown-up to help! Paint the boxes and draw on switches and cogs.

The eye test

Pat had just delivered some letters to Granny Dryden, one morning, when she called out after him.

"This one isn't for me, Pat," she said. "It is addressed to Miss Hubbard."

"Oh, dear," sighed Pat, as he peered closely at the envelope. "That's the second wrong delivery this morning. I couldn't have read the address properly."

Granny had a suggestion. "Get your eyes checked," she said. "Maybe your glasses need changing."

Pat nodded. "Good idea," he agreed. "I'll make an appointment."

So Pat arranged to have his eyes tested. The following day, he went into Pencaster to the opticians. He had been for an eye test before and knew what to expect.

First the optician put some strange frames on Pat's nose. Then he dropped different lenses into the frames.

"Read the letters on the card, please," he said to Pat,

He tried on lots of different frames. Some were smart and others made him laugh, when he saw himself in the mirror.

Finally, when Pat had decided on a pair, the optician told him to come back in a few days and his new glasses would be ready.

Pat could hardly wait. The same went for the people on Pat's round, who kept receiving the wrong letters!

But once Pat had his new glasses, they soon found their post arriving properly again.

"Thank goodness for that, Pat," they said.

Pat was rather pleased, too!

pointing to a card on the wall.

The letters were big at the top of the card and tiny at the bottom. Pat began to read down. But he did not get far.

The optician put another lens in the frame.

"That's better," said Pat, reading the letters down to the very last one.

Soon the optician knew exactly what sort of lenses Pat needed in his glasses.

"Perhaps you would like to choose new frames," he said.

"Okay," said Pat. He had been wearing his old frames for a long time. They were getting rather loose and kept slipping down his nose.

Shady Characters!

These pictures are called silhouettes.

Can you recognise the well-known Greendale characters from their silhouettes?

Goggle-box glasses!

Tom has made a pair of funny glasses. You could too, if you follow these instructions.

Trace shape A on to a piece of card. Ask a grown-up to cut out the shape. Don't forget to cut out two holes, so you can see!

Now trace shape B twice on to some card. Cut out the two shapes.

Tape the two arms on to the sides of the glasses.

Cut a cardboard tube in half. Stick the two halves over the eye holes using sticky tape.

Now you have your own pair of funny glasses. You could make a few more pairs and colour them in different colours.

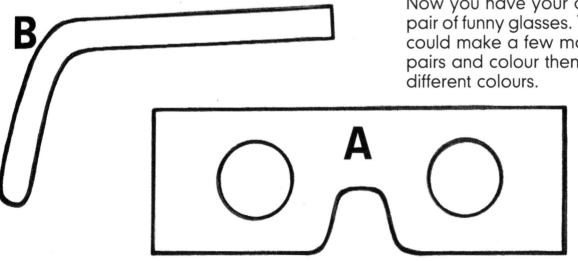

B

A

The History Lesson

1 Pat had been asked to give a talk to Julian's class. It was to be on the history of the post. He was busy reading about it from a book.

2 "There is a lot to find out, Jess," Pat smiled. "I hope Julian and his friends won't be bored by what I'm telling them." Soon it was time to go.

3 Pat drove to the school in his van and parked it in the playground. It was very cold. Pat felt nervous, as he hurried to the warm school.

4 Julian's teacher, Mrs Lake, met him outside the classroom. "The children are waiting for you," said Mrs Lake. "Come in." She opened the door.

5 Pat began his talk. He started by telling the children about the post boys. "They used to deliver all the mail on horse back," he explained.

6 Then he told them about the mail coaches, which could deliver post much faster than the post boys. All the children were very interested.

I still do that!

7 "But if it had been snowing and the roads were blocked," Pat went on, "the letters had to be delivered on foot. Just like I do now!"

8 "At about this time of year, a few of the coaches were decorated with holly," said Pat. He showed the children a colourful picture.

9 Finally, Pat held up a copy of the first postage stamp. "This was known as the Penny Black," he said. "It cost one penny, but is very rare now."

10 Afterwards, the children went out to play and Pat had tea with Mrs Lake. "The children enjoyed your talk very much," she said, smiling.

11 After he had drunk his tea, Pat collected his things and went out to his van. Then he laughed, when he saw the surprise waiting for him.

12 The children had decorated his van with holly. "It looks like the coaches of old days!" chuckled Pat, as they all thanked him.

Strange stamps!

Here are three sets of special Greendale stamps.

Can you see any differences between each set?

THE STORM!

Really?

1 It had been a very windy night in Greendale. Mrs Goggins had some bad news for Postman Pat, when he arrived at the Post Office.

2 "The railway line has been blocked by a fallen tree," she explained. "And this morning's mail train has been unable to get through."

3 Pat decided to pick up the mail from the train. "What a mess," he gasped, looking around at all the broken trees. He soon spotted the train.

4 When Pat had collected the post, he asked the guard if he could sort it all out on the train. "Of course you can, Pat," replied the guard.

5 By the time Pat had posted all the letters and parcels, it was lunchtime. "You are late today, Pat," said the Reverend Timms, looking surprised.

6 "I know, it's all these trees," Pat told him. "A lot of the roads are blocked and I've had to walk most of the way. My poor feet are aching."

7 On the way home, Pat spotted Ted cutting up a tree. "Can I have some logs to take home please, Ted?" he asked. Ted Glen nodded.

8 At home, Pat made up a nice fire with the logs. "I knew something good would come out of today!" he said, settling down for a snooze.

Desert Island Dreams

Pat is dreaming his favourite dream.
But what else do all his favourite things have in common.

Clue: make a list of the things in the picture.

Pat has lots of different things to deliver today. Julian has been sent a Christmas card. Granny Dryden is expecting a parcel, while Peter Fogg looks forward to his airmail letter. The twins have ordered their favourite comic and Reverend Timms is waiting for a letter. PC Selby doesn't know that a postcard is on its way. Match the villagers with their post.

The post round

The Church Parade

The postman's next stop was the vicarage. But the vicar was not there. Instead, Pat heard him mumbling from behind the vicarage wall. "Dear oh dear."

When Pat looked over the wall, he saw a worried-looking Reverend Timms struggling with a large flag.

"What do you have there?" asked Pat.

"It's the Boys Brigade's flag.

When Pat arrived at Colonel Forbes house, he was surprised to see him looking rather glum.

"What's up?" asked Pat.

"Oh, I found my old uniform," replied the colonel. "I was just thinking."

Pat smiled. "You miss your soldier days, don't you?" The colonel nodded.

"Why don't you try on your uniform. I'd like to see it," said Pat. The colonel's face soon brightened.

"Right," he said.

Pat sat in the armchair and waited. When he heard the colonel marching into the room, he stood up and said, "Halt!"

Colonel Forbes stopped smartly and saluted. Then they both burst out laughing.

Pat looked at his watch. "Goodness," he cried. "Look at the time. I must go and finish my round."

hey are marching on Sunday
and they want me to hoist the
flag. I'm practising but I'm in a
ness." The flag landed on
he vicar's head. "See?"

"'Let me try," said Pat. The
postman jumped over the wall
and tried to put the flag back
on to the ropes. But it was not
as easy as it looked.

"Don't worry. I know
someone who can help,"
smiled Pat.

Back at Colonel Forbes
house, the colonel was
surprised to see Pat again.

"It's the Reverend Timms,"
said Pat. "He's in a spot of
bother." He quickly explained.

"Can you help?" said Pat.
The colonel clipped his heels
smartly together, saluted and
answered with a smile, "Right
away, sir!"

At the church parade, the
band played and the boys
marched. Pat watched as
Colonel Forbes hoisted up the
flag perfectly. Then the colonel
saluted Reverend Timms, who
beamed and waved back.

"What a successful day,"
smiled Reverend Timms.
"Thanks, Pat."

"All in a day's work,"
laughed Pat.

The Royal Visit

Lovely.

1 Miss Hubbard was all dressed up, one day. "Do you like this new outfit?" she asked Pat, as she swirled in front of a mirror.

2 "Lovely," said Pat. "Are you going to a wedding or something?" Miss Hubbard smiled. "No, I'm off to see royalty!" she laughed.

3 She showed Pat a story in the paper. "The princess is coming to Pencaster," she explained. "I'm going along to cheer."

4 "What do you think of that, Jess?" laughed Pat, driving home. "I would love to see the princess, too." But Jess did not seem interested.

5 Next day, in Greendale, everyone was talking about the royal visit. "Well, I shall go," said Mrs Goggins, showing Pat a smart new hat.

6 On the big day, Ted Glen drove everyone into Pencaster in a bus. "I wish I could come," sighed Pat, waving them off, sadly.

7 Greendale was very quiet, as Pat went off on his round. "They have all gone to see the princess," said Pat, feeling left out.

8 Suddenly, a police motorbike drove into the village. "How strange," thought Pat. "That policeman does not look like a local chap."

9 The policeman needed some help. "There is a traffic jam on the motorway and I need to find another way to Pencaster."

10 Of course, Pat offered to help. He drew a little map. "Thank you," said the policeman, driving back the way he came.

11 A few minutes later, the same policeman appeared again. He was followed by a very smart car. Pat gasped in surprise.

12 "It's the princess! Look! She's waving to us. When the others get back from Pencaster, they will never believe me!"

Have you read Alice in Wonderland?

In this story, a bad-tempered Queen rules an army of playing cards. Katy is dressed as one of the card people.

You will need a large cardboard box.

Ask a grown-up to cut out two sides to make the back and front.

Attach two pieces of string to the top corners, so the cardboard hangs from your shoulders.

Paint the card black and white, then decorate with red hearts. Wear red trousers or tights and a red top.

Pat's Delivery Round

Help Pat deliver the Christmas post.

5

4

6
Colonel Forbes
is out.
Back to 4.

7
Mee
Selb
the villa
Forward t

3
No post for
Thompson Ground.
Forward to 5.

2

Coffee break
Granny Dryde
Back to 8.

1
Heavy sack slows
you down.
Miss one turn.

Post Office

ou need a dice and a counter for each player. Start at the Post Office and move
round the board, reading the instructions on the squares. The first player to reach
ome is the winner.

18 Lift from Peter Fogg. Forward to 19.

19

20

17

21 Heavy parcel for Rev Timms. Miss one turn.

16 Flat tyre. Back to 15.

22

15

23 Post sack is empty. Forward to win!

13 Very little traffic. rward to 15.

14

24

Home

Dance-along-with-Pat!

Here are a few dances you could try at parties.

The Conga

You need a few friends to do this one with. Hold the person in front of you, on the hips. Now the leader marches around, kicking one leg in the air every other step.

The Hand Jive

You can do this one sitting down, if you are tired of dancing. Pass your right hand over your left and back again, twice.

Tap your left fist onto you right fist, twice. Now repec this with the other hand.

Tap your left elbow with your right hand, twice. Now tap your right elbow with your left hand, twice. It is easy once you practise for a while.

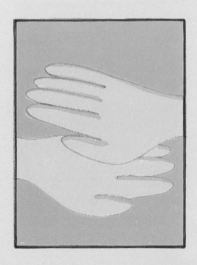

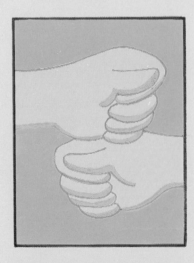

The Postman Pat Song

ostman Pat
ostman Pat
ostman Pat and his black and white cat
arly in the morning
ust as day is dawning
e picks up all the post-bags in his van

ostman Pat
ostman Pat
ostman Pat and his black and white cat
l the birds are singing
nd the day is just beginning
at feels he's a really happy man

erybody knows his bright red van
l his friends will smile
s he waves to greet them
aybe, you can never be sure
ere'll be . . .
nock! Ring!
tters through your door

ostman Pat
ostman Pat
ostman Pat and his black and white cat
l the birds are singing
nd the day is just beginning
at feels he's a really happy man
at feels he's a really happy man

Post Music 1982

The one-man band

Sam Waldron was in Greendale with his mobile shop, when he spotted Pat talking to Ted Glen.

"Would you like some tickets for the Pencaster Town Band concert?" asked Sam. "It's next Tuesday."

"I'd like to go," said Pat.

"Me, too," said Ted.

So they bought some tickets.

"Are you going, Sam?" asked Pat.

Sam chuckled. "I'll be there," he said, "up on the stage. Watch out for me."

Pat and Ted looked at one another, after Sam had gone.

"I didn't know Sam was in the band," said Pat.

"Neither did I," said Ted.

The following Tuesday, Pat and Ted drove to Pencaster. There was a crowd waiting to go into the town hall.

"Keep your tickets," said the man on the door. "Each one has a lucky number."

"What's the prize?" asked Postman Pat.

"It's a surprise!" smiled the man. Pat and Ted found their seats and watched the band get ready.

"I don't see Sam," said Pat.

Soon after, the band began a cheerful march followed by some foot-tapping tunes. Pat and Ted were soon enjoying themselves. But they could not understand where Sam was.

Then it was time for the band to take a break.

"I'd like to conduct a band," said Pat. "It must be fun."

Suddenly, the bandleader stepped forward. "Ladies and gentlemen," he said. "We have a special act to entertain you now. It is a one-man band!"

And on walked Sam.

"Gracious!" gasped Pat. Sam's one-man band outfit included a big drum, two cymbals tied to his knees, a harmonica in front of his mouth and a banjo in his hand.

Boom — boom — boom! went the drum. And in no time, everybody was clapping.

At the end of Sam's act, everyone cheered.

"Well done, Sam!" shouted Pat and Ted. "What a surprise!"

But there was another surprise in store for Pat.

"And now the lucky ticket number," said the bandleader. "Number ninety-nine!"

"That's mine!" cried Pat. "I wonder what I have won!"

"Two free tickets for the next concert," said the bandleader. "And a chance to conduct my band right now!"

Pat hurried on the stage and the conductor gave him his stick. Soon, the band began to play.

"What a marvellous evening," thought Pat, as he conducted the band. "I can't wait for the next concert!"

DO-IT-YOURSELF

1 "This bedroom ceiling really needs painting," thought Pat. "I'll do it myself. Now, what colour would be nice? Bright yellow, I think."

2 Pat went straight out and bought a large tin of paint and a brand new paintbrush. "This should not take me too long," he thought.

3 But painting a ceiling was not as easy as Pat had first thought. "Oh, dear," he sighed. "I keep getting yellow spots on my glasses."

4 By the time Pat had finished, he cou hardly see where he was going. "Oops!" he cried, putting his foot into the bucket of paint.

5 "Now I shall have to paint the floor," sighed Pat, looking at the mess. "And it will have to be exactly the same colour yellow as the ceiling."

6 So Pat painted the floor. But he managed to get spots on the walls. "Never mind," he decided. "They make a rather nice pattern."

7 Pat was quite worn out after all his work. It had taken much longer than he had expected. "I think I'll watch television now," he smiled.

8 But it was a programme all about how to decorate properly. "Maybe I should have watched this before I started!" chuckled Pat.

I Spy . . .

Miss Hubbard is busy decorating her lounge.

How many things beginning with the letter p can you spy in this picture?

Peppermint creams

While Pat is busy decorating, Julian and Sara make some of his favourite peppermint creams as a surprise.

You will need 200g of icing sugar, one egg white and a few drops of green food colouring and peppermint essence.

1 Whisk the egg white in a bowl until it is frothy.

2 Add a few drops of peppermint flavouring and food colouring.

3 Add the icing sugar to make a stiff mixture.

4 Knead into a smooth mixture and roll out to about ½cm thick.

5 Use a spoon or a rounded knife to cut out your initials and your friend's initials.

6 Arrange on a sheet of greaseproof paper and leave in a warm place for a day.

Remember
Always ask permission before cooking.
Always wash your hands first.
Always clear up afterwards.

Pat's Pencaster round

Bye!

1 Pat was going to help out with a post round on a new estate in Pencaster. Another postman was doing the Greendale round, in his place.

2 Sara and Julian waved, as he set off in the van. "Have a nice day!" they cried. "Thanks," said Pat, laughing. "It should be quite easy for me."

3 Pat felt happy as he drove. "There will be no steep hills, no lost sheep and no narrow winding lanes on the round in Pencaster," he told Jess.

4 Pat arrived at the estate and looke at all the letters. "These won't take me long to deliver," he said, as he set off. But he had a surprise in store

5 Things were not as simple as Pat had thought. All the numbers were in funny places. "Oh, dear," Pat thought, "this is tricky." He wandered about.

6 Soon Pat found he was lost. "I hope I manage to find the houses soon or the post will be late," he said, sighing. "Greendale was never this hard!"

7 A dog started to follow him. "Are you lost, too?" asked Pat, looking at the collar tag. "I'd better take you home." Pat found the right house.

8 The owner was very pleased to see her dog again. "He's always going off," she said. Then she showed Pat how to find some of the streets.

9 Pat was able to deliver more of the post, but he still had trouble. "This is the second time we have been here," he told Jess, as they drove round.

10 Finally, he had to deliver some letters to a large block of flats. The lift had broken, so Pat had to climb up the stairs. It was very hard work.

11 By the time he had finished, it was really late and Pat was exhausted. "This round was much more difficult than my normal one!" he puffed.

12 "Was it easy then?" asked Sara, as she brought Pat a cup of tea. But Pat said nothing. He was already asleep in his chair!

Pat's post puzzler!

Which path does Pat need to help him deliver this letter to number 8?

Julian's Bon Voyage

"Come and read this letter," called Julian, arriving home from school.

"It's about a trip to France for Julian's class," read Sara.

"I'm sorry, Julian. We can't afford a foreign holiday," Pat sighed, giving Julian a hug.

Julian looked upset.

"Hold on," said Sara. "It will only cost the price of the train and ferry. Julian will stay with a French family. Then a French child will come to stay here."

So it was agreed that Julian

could go on the trip. He would have to save his pocket money for spending, but there were still a few weeks to go.

"You can earn it by doing a few odd jobs around the house," smiled Sara.

By the day of the trip, Julian had saved ten pounds. The children had arranged to meet the teachers at nine o'clock. At half past eight, Pat was waiting in the hall.

"Come on, Julian. We will miss the coach."

"I can't go," wailed Julian. "I've lost my spending money."

Along came Sara. "It's a

good job I put it in a safe place for you," she said, holding up his piggy bank.

They loaded Julian and his bags on to the bus and waved goodbye.

"Bon voyage!" shouted Pat, which means *have a good journey* in French.

And Julian did have a bon voyage. They went on a ferry across the Channel and spent a week in Paris. Julian's exchange friend was called Francois.

It was difficult to get to know each other, as Julian could not speak French and Francois could not speak English.

"Fork," said Julian, holding up a fork.

"Fourchette," said Francois, pointing to the same fork. By the end of the week, they were firm friends.

Francois waved goodbye to Julian, as the coach left.

"Bon voyage!" called Francois, smiling.

"I know what that means," laughed Julian. "I have a clever dad."

"I didn't know your dad could speak French," said a surprised teacher.

Julian had been puzzling what to buy Pat as a souvenir.

"I know now," he beamed. "A French phrase book, so he can speak to Francois when they meet!"

Pat is learning to say some words in French. Here are a few for you to learn.

cow
vache (say vash)

horse
cheval (say shev al)

dog
chien (say she an)

cat
chat (say shat)

hello
bonjour (say bon juer)

ducks
canards (say can ards)

goodbye
au revoir (say oh rev war)

rabbit
lapin (say la pan)

thank you
merci (say mare si)

The Posting Game

How to play:

Each player must make three small letters. Now take it in turns to roll the dice and move that number of spaces.

If you land on a house, leave one of your letters there.

If there is already a letter at that house, you cannot leave yours.

The object of the game is to leave all your letters at different houses and reach home.

If you reach home without delivering a letter, go back and start again.

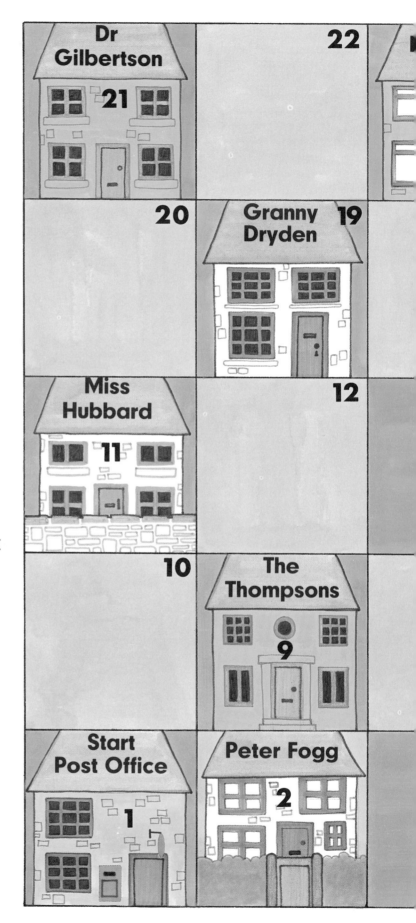

Daydreaming

1 Pat often leaves the van and walks to the little farms off the main road. "We don't want to get the van stuck in the lanes, do we?" he would say.

2 On these days, Pat would often stop for a while and daydream. Once he even decided he would write a book. "I could be famous," he thought.

3 "What do you think, Jess?" he said. "An adventure story all about the high seas? I could make it about me and call it Pirate Pat."

4 But Jess was too busy snoozing to take any notice. "Or I could write a mystery play about a famous detective and call it Private Eye Pat."

5 He looked around at the open spaces and smiled. "What about Pat the Explorer? It would make a great film." Jess just meowed.

6 The more Pat thought about being a writer, the more excited he became. "Trouble is, Jess," he sighed. "I don't know anything about exploring . . ."

7 ". . . or pirates . . . or detectives. In fact, all I really know about is being a postman. Come on, Jess. It's time we were going back home."

8 "Maybe I won't become a famous writer," he said. "After all, I'm sure no one wants to read about Pat the postman." But how wrong he was!

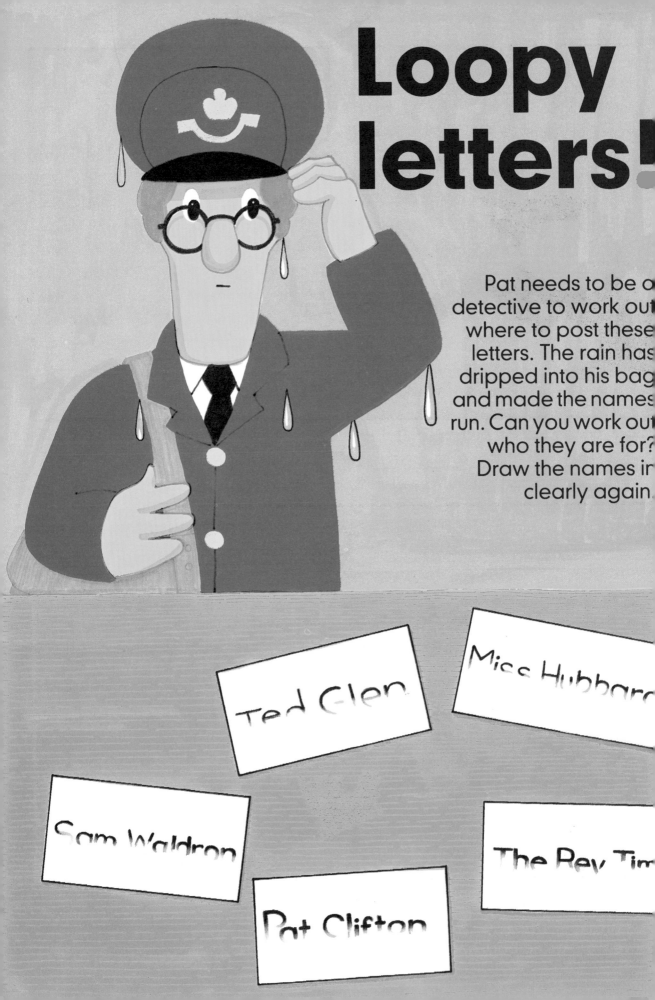

Loopy letters!

Pat needs to be a detective to work out where to post these letters. The rain has dripped into his bag and made the names run. Can you work out who they are for? Draw the names in clearly again.

Ted Glen

Miss Hubbard

Sam Waldron

The Rev Tim

Pat Clifton

Ship Ahoy!

In his daydream, Pat imagined he was a pirate. Can you find ten pieces of silver and five golden vases hidden in this treasure trove?

Make up a special name for Pat's secret island of treasure.

Strange noises!

Pat had offered to look after Colonel Forbes dog, Snap, while the colonel went on holiday. Pat was quite looking forward to having an extra animal in the house.

"You're a nice little dog," said Pat, on the first evening, as he ruffled Snap's fur. "Come on, time for a walk before bed."

Snap jumped up from his basket and ran to the door. He loved walks and wagged his tail eagerly. Pat went to fetch the lead from the cupboard.

"Won't be long, Sara," called Pat, shutting the door behind him. Pat did not notice Jess slip out of the door, too.

A little way along the road Pat found an empty field and let Snap off the lead.

"Off you go, Snap," he said "Have a run around." Pat picked up a stick and threw i calling "Fetch!"

Snap shot off into the darkness and Pat waited for him to return. But after a few minutes, he started to worry.

"Where can that dog be?" he puzzled. He wandered around the field for a few

inutes but there was no sign f Snap at all. He began to alk back home. Pat was set. How could he lose Snap n the first evening?

Just then, Pat heard a faint stling noise coming from a earby bush. It was too dark see what was there, so he alked closer.

"Is that you, Snap?" he lled, peering into the bush. ddenly, Pat heard another ise behind the tree.

"Snap, are you playing ames with me?" he asked, oving towards the tree.

Just then, he saw a small ape run from behind the tree, Pat chased after it.

Pat followed the trail of ses all around the village.

He was soon out of breath but just as he was about to give up, Pat arrived at Colonel Forbes manor house.

"There he goes!" cried Pat, seeing a shadowy shape run towards the front door of the house. Pat hurried after it but when Pat reached the door, it was not Snap he found — it was Jess!

"What are you doing here?" Pat wondered, scratching his head. He was very confused. Then he noticed Snap curled up in the doorway, fast asleep.

"So, Snap came back home," laughed Pat, "and you led me to him, Jess. What a clever cat you are. Come on, Snap, you are coming home with us tonight!"

PC Selby's tips for a healthy dog

1 Exercise
make sure your dog has plenty of long walks. This will keep it fit and happy.

2 Diet
try not to overfeed your pet. Most dogs only need one meal a day.

3 Cleanliness
do not bath your dog unless it is particularly dirty. Just use a brush to keep your pet in tip-top condition.

4 The vet
at any sign of illness, take your pet straight to the vet.

Make a pet dog

You will need: a cardboard tube, a cardboard egg box, some paper, paints and sticky tape.

1 Cut out a circle of paper. Cut it into the middle and twist it into a cone shape. This is the nose.

2 Stick the nose on to the cardboard tube. Add a paper tail and four egg box legs.

3 Paint your dog and stick on coloured eyes and ears.

Dotty drawing

Whose is this friendly face?
Join the dots and find out.

Jess meets a dinosaur

1 "What shall we do today?" asked Pat, one rainy Saturday morning. "We could go to the museum?" Julian suggested. Pat quickly agreed.

2 They called for Katy and Tom Pottag
on the way. "I'm afraid you must sta
in the van, Jess," said Sara, as they
pulled up outside. Jess was very sac

3 In the museum, they saw stuffed animals, sea creatures and lots of other interesting things. "What lovely shells," said Katy Pottage.

4 "I can see some butterflies," Tom smiled. "And I can see Jess," said Julian, frowning. "He must have followed us inside the museum."

But there were so many interesting things to see, they soon forgot about Jess. "Hey, look at that enormous dinosaur," gasped Tom Pottage.

6 "And look at its huge mouth!" cried Julian. But Pat had heard something that worried him. "I think I can hear Jess crying," he thought.

They all listened hard. The sound was coming from the inside of the dinosaur's mouth. Pat spotted a ladder and had a horrid thought!

8 They quickly ran to fetch an assistant. "I'm afraid my cat has managed to climb into the dinosaur's mouth and get stuck," explained Pat.

9 Pat climbed the ladder carrying a torch. "Jess!" he called. "It's me. I've come to rescue you. Don't worry." "Meow," came a sad little reply.

10 Julian was worried. "Jess must be very scared in there," he told Ton Pottage. "It must be really dark inside that big dinosaur."

11 Suddenly, a little black and white cat wandered out from behind the dinosaur. Pat could not believe it. "B . . but it's Jess!" he gasped.

12 "Trust you," Pat smiled. "Jess just didn't want to be left out of anything," laughed Julian. "You can come down now, dad!"

Mix and match!

Museums often have pieces of pottery which are thousands of years old. Can you help Colonel Forbes match up these broken pieces? Is there an odd piece?

Pat's bumper quiz

How carefully have you read this annual?

1 What was the name of Julian's French friend?

2 Who carried the flag at the church parade?

3 What colour did Pat paint his bedroom?

4 Sara dressed up as the Queen of Hearts. Who was Julian?

What is the name of the dance where everyone stands in a line, one behind the other?

6 Who let Pat have some logs for his fire?

7 Who was hiding behind the dinosaur?

8 What did Peter Fogg use to make a pretend horse?

9 Did Colonel Forbes dress up as Will Scarlet?

10 What are the Pottage twins called?

11 What was the name of the first postage stamp?

12 What is Julian's teacher called?

Answers

1) Francois 2) Colonel Forbes 3) yellow 4) the knave of hearts 5) the conga 6) Ted 7) Jess 8) his tractor 9) no, Colonel Forbes was the Sheriff, Tom played Will Scarlet 10) Tom and Katy 11) Penny Black 12) Mrs Lake